D1267694

Swapping Up For Beginners

Judith Housel

Isban Publishing

Dedicated to

Kyle MacDonald

Who wrote the unusual book

One Red Paperclip.

He Swapped Up from

a red paper clip

to a house in Kipling, Canada.

If you have not read it yet

It is not too late.

Should you find the premise of this book to be fascinating, then keep in mind that you may give a review at Amazon Books. Stars and Reviews are the life and death of a book. Your attention to this small detail will be greatly appreciated.

Here is an account based on the events in the life of Hugh, who recovered a tiny antique bottle from a packrat's nest. The boy traded the bottle for a painted rock and then switched the stone for another item. He kept swapping up until he acquired the object he wanted.

Table of Contents

Introduction

$1,000,000

Have you ever played the outdoor game bigger and better? Young people have an enjoyable time doing this for hours. They start with a small object and find someone who is willing to trade. The objective is to acquire something better with each exchange. They continue, repeating and repeating until they finish with something valuable. Swapping up could become your passion, too.

This is an introduction to swapping up. Participating in this activity will help give you confidence in the knowledge that you, too, can trade up to get the things you want. If this appeals to you, then why not go for it.

Discover how to do it

Right Here!

Chapter One

Tiny Bottle

For a century, the tiny bottle had lain in the desert sand, where a pioneer lost it along the way. Who knows who lost it! Perhaps it fell from a knap-sack jammed full of necessities. Nothing bothered it. The rare desert rain did nothing, and the blazing hot sun just peeled away the label pasted on the side of the bottle.

The summer heat was unbearable for any living things. In

this Sonoran desert, where massive Saguaro thrive, the heat can be deadly. Animals lived in holes in the ground to avoid the heat. Underground is the ideal place to be hidden. Rabbits, chipmunks, mice, prairie dogs, and rats only come out of their holes to find food in the cool of early mornings or evenings.

On just such an incredible evening, a packrat just happened to be digging around when she came upon the tiny bottle. She dug it out, and being a packrat, she carried it home to her nest, which was packed solid with hundreds of items. She jammed the bottle in with the rest of her treasures and scurried out to see what else she could find.

The dust flew near her head as a Red-Tailed Hawk whizzed past, just barely missing her. Instead, it hit and splattered the dry sand. The packrat leapt high and made a streak back to her lair. Hugh saw where she went and followed to investigate further. In the moonlight, Hugh got a glimpse of her location and began to dig for her treasure. Packrats always hoard treasures they find in the desert. The sand went flying through the air as the inquisitive boy flung dirt this way and that.

Eventually, Hugh found the packrat nest, which was a treasure trove. It was a bramble of twisted sticks, leaves, thorns, twigs, and various lost debris. Smack dab in the middle sat the old dirt-encrusted tiny bottle. Hugh picked it up and stuffed it into his pocket with his two pebbles and a piece of string.

The next day Hugh took a nice walk around the rural area where he lived with his parents in the Sonoran Desert. What was the reason for the arid conditions? Hugh's desert only received seven inches of rain each year. Compare that to the Big Island of Hawaii, where an inch of warm tropical rain falls every day.

The sun beat down on the dusty road. Hugh could see some tall trees as a bit of oasis surrounding the house of his nearest neighbor, Sue. Her adobe house was a half-mile away from the mobile home of Hugh and his parents. When Hugh approached the house, he saw Sue, who was calling her dog to quit barking. You would think that Shep would recognize Hugh and keep still. But country dogs sometimes get bored and bark at well-known people just for the Halibut.

Hugh called out, "Good morning Miss Sue. What's new with you?"

She replied, "It's another beautiful sunny day, just a little too hot. Maybe glorious heavy rain will break the drought. What do you think?"

Hugh reached in his pocket and pulled out the tiny bottle thrusting it in front of Sue's face. "Look what I found in a packrat's nest last evening. It is all dirty and gross, but do you think it might be valuable?"

"It sure looks old enough to be an antique and a small treasure at that," she said. "By the way, I saw a sign that made me think of you down on Taurus Drive. I was out early this morning taking a little walk when I noticed a placard on a stick. It is near the road stuck in a miniature sand dune."

Hugh asked Sue what it was. But she just said that he would have to mosey on over there to find out for himself. Hugh patted the tiny bottle in his pocket, saying, "OK, see ya later," and started walking in the direction of the mystery sign. The wind blew particles of sand into his eyes, but he kept going to find out what the mystery sign said.

Chapter 2

Spread Joy

Hugh walked down the shoulder of Sagittarius Road and over on Taurus Drive, where he saw the mystery sign in Miss Ellie's yard. She was bringing in bedsheets off the clothesline as the wind whipped them around and splattered them with unwanted sand.

As he walked up to her, she said, "Well, fancy seeing you here, Hugh. Did you happen to see the sign in our yard?"

He answered, "Yes, I did, and I sure would like to see that bike."

"It is right over here in the shed," she said as she grabbed the handlebars pulling the bicycle out for him to see. "You know Maggie can no longer ride the bike, now that she is confined to her wheelchair, so she plans to get rid of it. She's asking $260, and you know it is an expensive bike and practically new."

Hugh was drooling over the name-brand bicycle. "Man, wouldn't that be super to be riding this one all over the place! The problem is, I don't have any money. All I have are my two little rocks and this antique bottle that I retrieved from a packrat nest just last evening."

Hugh heard the screen door opening and saw a wheelchair maneuvering in the doorway. He looked as Maggie rolled out the door of the house trailer and asked to see the antique bottle. She was all dolled up in her emerald-green flowery dress and resplendent with gold necklaces. She also wore bracelets on her thin wrists and sported dangly earrings. Her dress accentuated her bright Lucile Ball red hair and brought out her stunning green eyes.

Hugh handed over the bottle for Maggie to see and listened as she made a suggestion. She told him that there might be a way for him to get the bicycle after all. She said that Frank collects antique bottles and might be interested in this old one.

"Listen, Hugh," she said, "Have you ever heard of swapping up? It is a method where a person trades a small object for one that is slightly better. He exchanges that thing for something else. He trades and swaps. He keeps repeating this gambit over and over and over until he ends up with something precious."

"You mean like your bicycle!" Hugh exclaimed.

Maggie stated, "Yes, indeedy, young man."

Hugh had an idea. He came up with, "Supposing, I did that swapping up gambit. What item of value would you like me to bring to swap for your bike?"

Maggie waved her boney arms around in the air. "Jewelry! You can plainly see that I am enthralled with jewelry!"

"I will give it a whirl! Beginning right now," said Hugh as he hastily started down their driveway, headed for Frank's trailer. As an afterthought, he turned to wave goodbye to the two ladies. They cheered him on, "Good luck Hugh!"

He was kicking up dust as he tried to remember which road

led to Frank's ancient beat-up trailer. The sides of the straight roads had large ditches, and the three-acre lots had masses of dry, dead-looking scrub brush. Here and there amongst the creosote bushes were short, small half-dead mesquite trees. The prolonged drought had been harsh on the withering landscape.

The area was sparsely settled, with house trailers very far apart. Hugh would have to walk miles to go from one abode to another and home again.

When he got to Frank's old, dilapidated trailer, he hollered, "Hello, there, Frank!" While standing in the yard, he observed some rusty pieces of antique farm equipment scattered here and there. There were five worn-out trucks and cars parked where they gave up the ghost amongst the dead weeds. The vehicles seemed as dead as the dried-out vegetation.

Hugh was wondering if this swapping idea would even work for him. Maybe trading up is a silly pastime after all. He persevered, though. "Finish what you start," as they say.

After a wait, Hugh knocked loudly on the side of the metal trailer house. He beat on it with his mighty fist. He heard a shuffle, shuffle sound, and the door creaked slowly open. There was rickety old Frank with an expansive grin on his face saying, "Come on in, quickly, quickly. Don't let the stifling hot air inside."

Frank motioned to the window shelves lined with a

variety of old bottles and worn antique objects. "Lookie here! These are only some of the bottles I have around the place."

Hugh examined the bottles as he continued listening to Frank talking. "Maggie just called to say you were on your way over here. She said that you had never heard of the trading up thing. Well, have I got a treat for you? See, there is this guy from Canada named Kyle MacDonald who began with one red paperclip. He traded it for something better and kept trading and swapping until he ended up with a house in Kipling, Canada. Can you believe that? Well, it is true, I guarantee you. Here is a copy of his non-fiction book that I am willing to loan you (mind you, I said loan, not give).

Please bring it back straight away when you have finished reading it. OK?"

Frank continued speechifying, "Now, let me see your tiny bottle if you don't mind." Hugh wondered how Frank knew about the tiny bottle.

Frank eyeballed the bottle and admitted that it would be a fine addition to his collection. "Would you like to trade? How about this yellow pencil?" Hugh thought it might be hard to trade an ordinary used pencil, so he said, "No, thank you. Do you have something different? I would prefer something else, a pretty item, maybe." Meanwhile, Hugh was thinking, "Do you have something without bite marks all over it?"

Frank showed Hugh a wooden clothespin, but the boy did not respond well to that, either. Hugh knew that the tiny bottle was worth way more than a wooden clothespin.

Hugh looked at all the junk on the table but was not impressed by anything he saw there. The bargaining material Frank was offering up was lame.

Then Frank suggested his small hand-painted rock. He reached behind a random pile of dusty papers to pull out a painted stone. He wiped and blew the thick dust off it before handing it over to Hugh to examine. "It is charming and just the thing that will be easy for you to swap with nearly anyone. Look at the artwork on it. The artist painted two words, *Spread*

Joy and two white dogwood flowers."

Hugh liked the hand-painted rock, and so they made the trade. Frank set the tiny bottle on the window shelf with a myriad of other strange objects. Hugh looked at the obscure collection everywhere in the little old house trailer. They sat together at the kitchen table chatting, quite a while about this and that and plenty of nothing. Hugh rolled the painted stone round and round in his fingers.

Frank asked, "Do you ever wonder what treasure is in the pot at the end of the rainbow? Your life could advance in bounty if you practiced this easy, simple way to obtain bigger and better things."

Hugh answered, "Yes, it would be mighty nice to have anything my little heart desires. I certainly do want to bolster my bounty."

Frank said, "If you have a dream of abundance in your life, this might be the sure-fire way to make it come true. Swapping up is a good way of doing it. First, have a dream, devise a plan, and next, carry it out."

Hugh got mighty few words in edgewise because, as you probably noticed, Frank likes to engage in his own style of banter.

Hugh commenced the long hot walk home through the whistling wind and dust and dirt. His hand holding Frank's book was sweating, and the pretty painted rock was safely tucked in his shorts pocket. He wondered when in the world the Monsoon rains would come and stop this devastating drought.

Hugh saw a slight movement over to his right. His eyes were quick to dart to the embankment along the right side of the road. The raised area, which ran along both sides of the gravel and caliche road, was created by the passing road grader. A critter with blinking eyes caught Hugh's attention at the roadside.

He stopped and bent over to peer into a four-inch hole in the embankment. He saw big eyes in a feathered face staring back at him. He thought he was looking at a Northern Saw-Whet Owl. On second thought, this little guy might be a Burrowing Owl.

He took his head out of the book for a few seconds as he reached into the mailbox to grab the paper envelopes inside. There was the electric bill which he was not interested in. Next was an envelope with neatly handwritten words on the front. Hugh read his name and address then his eyes turned to the return address. He focused on the name of his cousin, who lived up in Homer, Alaska.

When he stepped into the blue mobile home, he immediately looked up the fact that the distance from Silverbell, Arizona, to Homer, Alaska, was 3,909 miles. It was not merely far away, but Hugh had never been there.

Hugh informed his mom that a letter had arrived from his cousin, the one in Homer.

He read it out loud to her before he began telling her about his adventures.

Chapter 3

Minnie Mouse Cat Toy and.
See It & Say It in Spanish

When Hugh had his parent's total attention, he relayed to them about his whereabouts of the day. He had walked all the way from one side of the village to the other side and home again.

First, he recounted the meetup with the tiny owl. He told them he had a staring contest with an owl in a hole at the side of the road. Do you think the owl won?

He showed them the borrowed book, *One Red Paperclip*. He mentioned the bicycle that Maggie has for sale. "She is asking $260 for the bike," he said as he explained his new plan to swap with people until he could get the bike. They were wondering about the possibilities. Is it possible to make trades like this? They admired the hand-painted words on the black stone. His dad asked who would ever want such a thing, but his mom was sure someone would just love the sweet message on the rock and be anxious to trade something of value for it. They admired Hugh's determination to get the bicycle.

Dad said, "Boy, you have grit," and he tousled his son's mop of hair. Monty wondered if Hugh would persevere or quickly forget all about trading up.

Melanie said, "If a person stays occupied, he might as well dedicate his time to something profitable."

They read and reread the letter from their relatives in Alaska.

Mail rarely came from Alaska, so this was a special occasion. Hugh picked up a ballpoint pen from the small white pitcher where the family kept their writing pens and pencils.

Hugh slipped his writing tablet from its spot in the bookcase. He always kept it in the same exact location, so he never had to look for it.

He copied the name and address onto the long envelope he snatched from the desk. He began his letter by writing "Dear Cousin Paris." Half an hour later, it was ready to mail except for a school photo he wished to place in the envelope with the carefully written letter.

He scurried around, searching here and there for his photo. Finally, he found a picture of himself to include in the envelope. He took the backing off the sticky stamp and affixed it to the envelope's upper right corner.

That same evening the little family went to Lil's home for a fish fry. There were cats all over the yard. Some sat in trees while some sprawled across the cement patio, searching for a cooler resting spot in the shade on this hot afternoon. Other guests watched in amusement as Lil's young daughter, Tanya, was strolling around dragging a gigantic cat by the belly. Hugh spotted a couple of rowdy kittens wrestling under a faucet, a refreshingly cool area because of the moisture from the water spigot. Fully grown cats gave the evil eye to the tumbling carefree kittens as they disturbed their naps.

When Hugh told Lil, the lady of the house, about trading up for something bigger and better, she was enthralled. "Hey, "she said, "Let me see your pretty painted stone one more time," She rolled it around in her hands and admired it. "Here is what we will do," she said," Even though I would hate to see them go, I will be willing to trade (under duress, mind you) those two endearing kittens under yonder spigot! What do you say?"

Hugh's ecstatic youthful demeanor was quickly squashed. He saw the negative expressions and shaking heads of both his parents as a huge clue! They say, "Nope, no kittens!"

Hugh let it go when he noticed a stuffed Minnie Mouse cat toy lying under a creosote bush in the yard. The blowing wind was agitating the lightweight mini pillow toy as though it was about to float away.

He bent over to pick it up as he asked, "How about this toy? Would you like to trade it for the *Spread Joy* stone?" Lil looked at Minnie Mouse and twisted her bottom lip, thinking about such a serious subject. She glanced over at Tanya, and finally, she nodded. So, they made the trade, then and there. Lil and Hugh were both happy with the exchange, but someone else might not be so happy.

Walking around the spacious yard, Hugh picked up pieces of firewood from the ground. First, he brought little loads of kindling to the fire pit.

Someone built a miniature log cabin shape in the fire ring. It was a one-match fire when Tanya lit the piece of paper that was in the center of the little log house shape. She was proud of that accomplishment.

Hugh helped encourage the fire by poking it with a long thin stick of mesquite wood, preparing it to cook the fish. There were substantial fagots in a neat pile near the tall cottonwood tree. Everyone gathered around at a distance to enjoy the fire and help set up for the cookout. With the sun beating down, no one wanted to be too close to the hot fire. The cooking food smelled wonderful to the hungry group. The aroma of fish fillets grilling drew everyone to the grill. Even the cats came around asking for a little bit to share.

Lil, the lady of the house, made sure that she had her picture taken with Hugh and Minnie Mouse and the painted stone. The two of them posed as the sun lowered in a cheery, outlandishly colored western sky.

The little girl, Tanya, began to whine and tried to grab the Minnie Mouse toy out of Hugh's hand. Hugh held it up high where she couldn't grab ahold of it. Her distraught face told it all.

"Gimmie, my Minnie Mouse," she demanded loudly.

Hugh thought about how fortunate he was to be able to make trades right away. Two swaps in one day, how unexpected. Then the gentleman of the house, seeing the reaction from Tanya, stepped up with an idea.

He said, "I am enjoying the thought of your surefire swapping plan. I think you have the gumption to carry out what you have started. When you have finished reading *One Red Paperclip*, I plan to ask Frank if he will loan it to me next. As a matter of fact, I would enjoy making a trade with you myself. I see that Tanya is not happy to see Minnie Mouse leave. We might be able to appease her. He set down his plate of food and said, "Let me go into the house and have a look around right now. There is bound to be something that would be useful to you."

He returned shortly with a Spanish lesson book. Ever the bookworm, Hugh perked up when he saw the book *See It & Say It In Spanish.* When he looked inside the paperback, he did a little easy math. Hugh saw the date published by examining the front pages and calculated that the paperback was precisely sixty years old. "Oh," he said, "I love studying Spanish, and I adore this old book with the aged brown pages. I might just have to keep this tome forever." Someone said, "You can always make a xerox to keep for yourself." Hugh thought that was a great idea. Someone is thinking outside the box.

"Let's take photos of us swapping, too," Hugh said. The sky was already darkening, so they found a well-lit area to pose with the Minnie Mouse toy and the Spanish book. Lil and Tanya crowded in with the guys. Melanie pointed her flash camera at Hugh along with the man of the house standing near Lil. Tanya held her dad's hand on the other side. Melanie took a tender photo of them posed together. Lil showed off the painted stone while Tanya clutched the Minnie Mouse toy, and Hugh held the Spanish lesson book, *See It & Say It In Spanish*. The man of the house just held onto Lil with his left hand and Tanya with his right hand. Hugh stood on Lil's left with his head tilted down, reading his newly acquired Spanish book.

Staying in the light, Hugh had his face in the book immediately. The bookworm, on overdrive, flipped through the pages with intense interest. Meanwhile, Tanya was kissing Minnie Mouse and showing her to one cat after another.

At home later that night, with a full tummy and happy

thoughts, Hugh stayed up late, learning the Spanish language. How will he continue the swapping endeavor if he cannot bear to part with this one little paperback book?

Chapter 4

EL OSO

Hugh slept in on Saturday morning. When he woke up, he began speaking fluent Spanish. "Hola, Senora," he greeted his mom, who said, "Senor, I was fixing to go to town. Since you are awake, would you want to tag along?"

Hugh jumped at the chance. "May I bring the Spanish book and make xerox copies of the pages?"

"Yes, you may, Honey," said his mom. "Jump into your clothes, and let's get a move on." Melanie ran a comb through her straight brown hair and grabbed her purse and truck keys. She glanced at her hair in the mirror and realized she needed a haircut. "One of these days," she mumbled to herself.

Hugh found matching socks rolled together in pairs and his undies on the right side of his little drawer. He combed his teeth and brushed his unruly hair.

Water rushed out the faucet to splash the crackly sleep out of his eyes. His shirts were rolled up in the other drawer. The blue striped one looked perfect when he slipped into it. He searched in the hamper and put on his cleanest pair of dirty shorts.

They drove the thirty-five bumpy miles to Casa Grande and went straight to the copy shop where Hugh made copies of the book's old, tanned pages. Two hundred fifty-four pages divided by two equals 127 copies. At 5 cents each (127 times $.05) equals $6.35. That seemed like a lot, but Hugh was anxious to keep a copy of the well-designed book for himself.

His mom had a list of things to accomplish in town, so Hugh thought he would take advantage of his situation and continue swapping while visiting civilization. The next place they went shopping was the feed store owned by Melanie's friend. The laying hens at home needed a couple of sacks of laying mash. Hugh wandered around the store looking at expensive western saddles and rich-looking genuine leather cowboy boots. Nearby he noticed a can of EL OSO cream shoe polish for sale along with other odds and ends sitting on shelves.

When he showed the store owner his book and the xerox copies, she was interested in acquiring the Spanish lessons immediately. She said, "You know my daughter, Sissy, will be taking Spanish this Fall in the tenth grade. She will have a basic understanding of the language if she studies this book all summer long. Yes, sir, she would have a jump on her lessons."

Hugh started to hand her the actual book. She stopped him by saying, "Actually, I would prefer to take the sheets on typing paper. Sissy can punch holes in them and carry them in her binder."

Hugh agreed, and they immediately swapped. He ended up with a can of EL OSO cream shoe polish from the feed store shelf, making him happy as he thought it would be easy to trade for something else. In addition to that, he still had possession of the actual Spanish lesson book.

Before heading on, Mom snapped a shot of her friend standing with happy Hugh demonstrating the trade they made. She looked smug with the sheets of paper in her hands, standing beside Hugh with his metal can of EL OSO cream shoe polish. Do you think the store owner knew that she got the better part of the deal? You bet your sweet biffy she did.

With the bags of chicken mash in the bed of the truck, they drove to Melanie's next stop along the way. As they rolled down the road, Hugh had his face embedded in the Spanish book. The shoe polish can fit tightly in his pocket with two small stones and a piece of string.

Chapter 5

Big Magnifying Glass

They stopped at the Insurance Office, where Hugh asked each employee if they would like to swap anything. He asked all the people in the waiting room if they would be interested in trading something for the can of EL OSO shoe polish. The people were not the least bit interested in trading, but they did have plenty of gossip to spread around.

Hugh didn't want to hear gossip, so he sat in a chair and proceeded to look at the pictures in his Spanish book. He repeated the foreign words to himself, over and over again, to improve his language skills.

A pesky fly buzzed around his arm. When it became a real bother, a guy sitting nearby said, "Let me show you how to swat that fly. Sit very still. Don't move a muscle." The man held his two hands together above the resting fly. Then he separated them until his hands were about five inches apart. Then suddenly, he slapped his hands together. That annoying fly jumped straight up between his hands and got squashed. Hugh put that episode in his memory bank.

The next place on the schedule was the Tractor Supply Store. Now, this is a most exciting store. The farmer's store is loaded with all kinds of stuff you need, but then you could never know what you might need.

Hugh and Melanie made the rounds seeing what they wanted for the house. As Hugh came in contact with people, he asked them if they would like to swap something for his can of shoe polish. One wiseacre said yes, he would give up his empty Bic Lighter, but Hugh said, "No, thank you. I will keep my shoe polish just the same."

A lovely little old lady said she did not need reddish-brown shoe polish. A few minutes later, a clerk in the store said that she was too busy working right now, but maybe they could get together later. A polite kindhearted farmer said he needs shoe polish but, unfortunately, has nothing to trade at the moment.

Hugh put the can back into his shorts pocket. He felt a little discouraged.

They went grocery shopping last so the cold food would not get ruined on the long drive home. They put the frozen and cold food in the ice chest, which was in the bed of the pickup truck with the chicken feed. When Hugh and his mom were through grocery shopping, they jumped into the pickup and drove home. A strong wind was blowing the sand sideways across the road in front of them. The sandstorm blocked the view making it difficult to see very far down the road. Bushes were leaning over and whipping about in the strong wind. The young gentleman helped his mom put away the groceries. They put away the cold items first before stashing the rest of the food in the cupboards. Melanie noticed the grit on the food and in the grocery bags. Just part of living in the desert.

Hugh was a bit disappointed that he had not traded away the can of EL OSO cream shoe polish. In the tack room, he poured the laying mash into the barrel and secured the lid. Do you know the secret way to pull the string on a sack of feed? Do you have to pull the string a certain way to open the sack of feed?

Coming in the kitchen door, Hugh said, "I know what, Mom, let's go over to Heather and Sam's house. He is such a helpful guy, and he has tons of junk from which to choose. I will ask him if he wants to take this opportunity to swap with me."

Dad stretched as he got up off the couch. He said, "You two go out visiting while I certainly have another important TV show to keep an eye on."

They say, "Like Father, Like Son." In this case, Hugh is a bookworm, while his dad favors movies and TV shows. Marty wants to watch an old western movie starring John Wayne. He would rather watch a classic film than go visiting today.

Melanie and Hugh set out for Sam and Heather's house, just a mile away.

Dust billowed all about the truck as Mom turned into Sam's narrow driveway.

They sat on the freshly painted veranda with good

old Sam and his wife, Heather, whose health was doing poorly as usual. Heather said, "Thanks for dropping by to visit. We rarely see you guys. You will have to come by more often." Their wooden house is all color coordinated as though a professional designer had chosen the paint colors. The porch is a wrap-around style with French doors leading into the dining room.

"Shall we move inside," Heather said, "This wind is too much for me to handle."

So, they all left their lawn chairs where they stood and escaped from the wind, indoors where it was calm. As soon as they got inside, the chairs began to go sliding across the veranda floor. Two of them suddenly went flying away. Hugh and Sam leaped outdoors to capture the chairs and bring them inside.

The four talked about this and that until Hugh spoke about his plan to get the nearly new bike from Maggie. He brought up the subject with hopes of interesting Sam and Heather in a swap. Hugh relayed the news about his current swapping endeavors.

Sam wondered what item Hugh had up for trade at this moment. Hugh dug the can out of his pocket and displayed it to everyone in the living room. Sam began to show Hugh some of the many items that he might want to trade. None of the things looked good to Hugh. He said, "No," to a miniature plastic horse. He said, "No," to a child's game of pickup sticks. He said, "No," to a special pen that writes with green ink.

Hugh even said, "No," to a little electric bell that rings whenever an angel enters the room. They walked into Sam's office, where more items were sitting around, either on shelves or not on shelves. That is when Hugh's eyes locked onto a clear round glass circle with a handle. "What in the world is this thing?" He asked as he held it up in the air.

"That, my dear boy is a magnifying glass," Sam said. "Here we go. Let me show you how to look through it." He held it over a book with small print. Inside the glass circle, the image looked more prominent than it had a few seconds earlier. The small, printed words became large words like magic. Hugh was enthralled with the magnifying glass and asked, "Sam would you consider trading this magnifying glass for the brand-new can of EL OSO cream shoe polish?"

Sam was messing with Hugh when he said, "I don't know, it was a gift from my favorite Auntie. I don't think I can part with this crystal-clear magnifying glass. She would be crushed to find out that I don't appreciate her thoughtful gift. My Auntie would tan my hide and nail it to the shed if she discovered such treachery."

Do you still have plenty of other things you might be willing to swap?

They were befuddled for a few seconds.

Then Sam said, "I relent. I was just kidding. Of course, you can take the magnifying glass. You know that once someone gives you a gift, it is yours to do with as you wish."

Hugh thought about that one for a few moments, and then they traded with each other. A classic picture was taken with Sam and Hugh exchanging the can of EL OSO shoe polish for the magnifying glass.

As they were walking down the front steps, Hugh overheard his mom telling Heather that she should speak up if she ever needed anything. "Don't be shy," she said. Hugh thought, "Don't be shy. That is right. No need for me to be reserved, either."

Chapter 6

Red Flashlight

All day that Sunday, we find Hugh investigating everything he came across with the magnificent magnifying glass. He spied on bugs. He researched fabrics. He viewed hairs on his own arms and freckles on his dad. He even found out that his dad's freckles had freckles.

Melanie and Monty got a kick out of their busy son, checking out all the objects he came across. Mom remembered something that occurred when she was a teenager. She told Hugh and Monty the tale of a kid named Wilbur who nearly burned a house down. Wilbur carelessly laid his magnifying glass on a dresser in front of a bright sunny South-facing window in his bedroom. The lens focused the hot sunlight in one minuscule spot on stacks of papers directly underneath, causing them to heat up excessively. In a short while, the family smelled smoke and ran to the bedroom just in the nick of time. Smoke filled the air, and flickering flames formed faster than you could sing *Figaro* an opera buffa. Someone smacked out the fire and quickly removed the magnifying glass from the danger zone.

Hugh took that incident to heart and used all equipment in a safe manner. Hugh used his magnifying glass to read his Spanish book. It was so much fun. He used it as often as possible because he knew it must be swapped for something else if he expected to trade up to the beautiful bicycle in Maggie's shed.

Hugh asked his buddy Edwardo to take a walk with him. They ambled over to Maggie and Ellie's trailer just to visit. Ellie asked him, "Are you still planning to trade up to get Maggie's bike?"

"You bet I am," said Hugh. "I have already made a few trades, and I am on a roll. I see you still have the BIKE for SALE sign out at the edge of your driveway. Would you like me to bring it in for you?"

Both, Ellie and Maggie, nodded their heads, so the boys went out front and brought in the sign. They put it in the shed where Hugh showed the bike to Eduardo.

Eduardo said, "That bike is something else. You have a fantastic plan to get it."

While the boys walked around Silverbell, they had an interesting conversation.

Hugh explained the details of how he is swapping one thing for another. Each trade is supposed to be bigger and better. After many trades, Hugh wants to have some valuable jewelry to trade to Maggie in exchange for that beautiful bike.

Eduardo was fascinated. He said, "Hugh, if you can do it, I can do it, too. I just now decided I am going to do the same thing you are doing."

Hugh encouraged his buddy, and they expressed

daydreams of things they could accomplish. Even though each boy had twangs of bashfulness when approaching a stranger, they had to set that aside and speak up. They practiced speaking up. They practiced what words they would say when talking with people. It was something new to do, and they enjoyed doing it together.

As the boys walked around the neighborhood, they used the magnifying glass at every opportunity. They looked at leaves and insects. The thorns on Mesquite trees looked like dangerous daggers. Stink bugs resembled dinosaurs. They amazed themselves by the reality of nature. Eduardo told Hugh that he sure would like to have the magnifying glass.

"Well, I do plan to trade it. Tell me what you have to trade," Hugh said.

Eduardo said, "Let's drop by our trailer to see what we can see."

Amongst all kinds of material in the junk drawer, they found a small red flashlight that delighted Hugh. So, the boys traded right away. Eduardo's big sister took their photo, swapping the magnificent magnifying glass for a small red flashlight.

They continued talking about the value of bigger and better. Eduardo's big sister, Faustina, joined in the conversation and was enthralled. "You got me. I'm all in," she said.

Hugh said, "I am not extremely shy, but it is challenging for me to walk right up and talk to someone I don't know very well."

Eduardo said, "Me too."

Faustina told them, "Don't worry, boys. If you force yourself to talk to strangers, you will get used to it. Pretty, soon speaking up will become second nature to you. After all, a stranger is just a friend you have not met yet."

Faustina returned to her house cleaning chores. That is how it is when you are older and more responsible. She put some towels in the washing machine. Then she ran hot water in the dishpan and piled it full of drinking glasses. She washed the glasses first because she wanted them to be sparkling clean. Next came the plates and dishes.

Faustina was daydreaming about the future possibilities of Swapping Up. In this way, time flew by, and her chores were quickly finished.

The boys resumed playing and looking at everything imaginable with the magnifying glass. Hugh looked in dark corners with the beam of the red flashlight. Faustina had to stop cleaning long enough to peer through the magnifying glass at the dirt and dust bunnies that came floating out from under the bed. All three young people were fascinated with the way objects appear when they look so big under the magical magnifying glass.

The next few nights, Hugh used the red flashlight to read *One Red Paperclip* late into the night. He sat at the kitchen table during the daytime, reading that book on trading up. Hugh had found an activity that fascinated him no end. Swapping, Trading, Wheeling and Dealing, Exchanging, Bartering or Switching. Whatever you call it, Bigger and Better is an experience to remember.

Hugh was in a good mood and so glad that Faustina and Eduardo were interested in Swapping Up.

Hugh was now dedicated to his new occupation, Swapping Up.

Chapter 7

Money-Saving Secrets
in a Paperback Book

Things drifted back to normal for Hugh until Wednesday afternoon, when scattered showers were visible miles and miles away creeping across the distant mountains. Here and there could be seen dark grey clouds moving across the hot, dry desert. The rain made slanted grey shapes so far away the movement was imperceptible. Hugh just stood and watched the violent activity in the sky as the colossal storm moved closer and closer.

Eduardo walked over to visit even though dark clouds were brewing on the horizon. They enjoyed the cool breezes and a bit of splashing from large cold raindrops here and there. As the scattered shower passed, Monty returned home from work. The boys ran up to him at the driver's door of the pickup.

Hugh shouted, "Dad, Dad! Did you see the rain we just had? We had two inches of rain!" They all looked at the dusty, parched earth. Sure, enough, the few raindrops that fell in the driveway dust were two inches apart.

Monty said, "You rascal, you!" He gave Hugh a knuckle rub in his thick hair and scalp.

All three guys went into the trailer and sat down for icy glasses of lemonade. A little fun banter ensued as they chatted about their days. Hugh and Eduardo were busy swatting flies with the hand-clapping technique. "This works like a charm," Eduardo said.

Monty wondered out loud, "How is it going with your swapping gig?"

Hugh said that he had no further exchanges. He seemed a bit blue over it. Everyone I speak to has no use for a little red flashlight.

At that moment, Mom spoke up. "I could use a little red flashlight to keep in the kitchen drawer."

Eduardo said in an encouraging voice, "Go for it, Hugh! Wait a minute. She did not even say what she has to exchange."

Mom started looking around. She grabbed a baseball and held it up. She looked intently at Hugh for a reaction. She got one in a split second when Hugh jumped up, saying, "Wait a minute. That is MY baseball!"

Everyone had a good laugh at that.

Melanie looked in kitchen drawers, she peered through the glass of her China cabinet, she looked on the shelves by the washing machine, she even filtered through the mess on the desk and in the desk drawers. Hugh didn't see a thing that was useful to him.

She looked at various items, searching for something that someone else would have a desire to own. Something practical. Something bigger and better than a little bitty flashlight. After a bit, she came upon a paperback book, *Extraordinary Uses for Ordinary Things*. It was concealed in a pile of papers, pamphlets, and books on the side table by the couch. "This is the perfect thing for you, Son. This book is highly desirable. It is just the sort of thing that will impress a housewife in Silverbell."

Hugh accepted it with a bit of doubt on his face. He felt that he had to try something different as there had been no luck with what he had to offer lately.

Dad took their photo as they exchanged the red flashlight for the unusual book. The switch was finalized with a handshake and a couple of bear hugs. Melanie and Hugh both looked good in their photo. Melanie flipped her little red flashlight on and off.

Hugh flipped through the book and was encouraged by some of the household activities he saw illustrated in it. People do love pictures. He looked at the illustrations in the book. There were instructions to use lemons around the house. He saw lots of things to do with vinegar and rubber bands. Ice cubes come in handy for many purposes.

Hugh became heartened again and had high hopes for being able to swap this book for something else, something bigger and even better.

With this new item, Hugh was anxious to start wheeling and dealing again. They all looked out the windows at the impending storm.

So far, there were only threats of a downpour, but the boys were tired of the hot, dry weather and were anxious for the Monsoons to start.

There was the possibility they would get a powerful shower and have the opportunity to run around in the rain.

Hugh and Eduardo went out for a pleasant walk. With a possibility of rain and cooler air blowing in, they whirled around, enjoying the smattering of drops from a mile above. The boys did run around in the light sprinkling as the sun lowered in the western sky. Halfway to Eduardo's home, they separated and turned toward their respective abodes, running with joyous abandon through the smidgen of liquid sunshine.

Hugh was not soaked to the skin when he arrived home, but it felt so good to have a little bit of moisture splattered on himself. He cooled down quickly as he took off his shoes at the door and began making plans for the following days.

Chapter 8

Cream Pitcher

A few days later, the boys got together with wheeling and dealing as their mission. Hugh asked, "Eduardo, are you planning to trade the magnifying glass?"

Eduardo replied, "Earlier, I did think I would, but not now. I want to keep it forever. Let's go back to my trailer. I'll find something to begin my swapping career."

Eduardo rummaged around his home until he found an acceptable object.

The friends carried small trading objects as they went walking farther from home. The wind blew, and clouds passed overhead. Dust filled the air, but they didn't care. They went up to each doublewide home and trailer they came to along the way. Some people were not home, but a few came to the door. Most yards looked desolate, but most had bushes or runty trees here and there.

They asked for trades, but the boys got one negative answer after another. They were not completely discouraged, though, because they knew that it just takes one interested person to effect a trade.

One man said he didn't need a housekeeping book because he never does anything around the house. Hugh glanced through the door at the littered dusty home and thought, that makes sense.

Eduardo stuck out his hand with the palm up to display a blue cat's eye marble for the guy to see.

The man said, "WOW, would you look at that! Now, that will fit perfectly in my little marble collection."

Eduardo got excited and asked him what he had to swap. The guy went inside his trailer. In a minute, the fellow returned to the door with his hands full of small items. Eduardo looked them over, and after asking a few questions about the stuff, he selected one quite fascinating object.

Hugh took an excellent photo of Eduardo making his first trade. The marble collector had a big happy grin on his gnarly face to match the wide grin on Eduardo's round face. They both had smiling eyes in the photo taken outside the man's trailer. Eduardo thought the item he got was an eye-opener.

As the two boys sauntered down the driveway, Hugh asked, "Shall we go back home? I am not having any luck today."

"Let's just try one more place on our way home." Eduardo implored.

Dust swirled as they went over to the place next door. They strolled up the gravel driveway of the tidy little trailer adjacent to the marble collecter's trailer. Enjoying the cool breeze whipping the hair from their skulls across their eyes and mouths, they both looked expectingly at the teal blue door in front of them. As the door slowly opened, the sweetest little lady you would ever want to meet greeted them. At the entrance, she gave them a wide generous, authentic smile.

When Hugh and Eduardo introduced themselves, she said, "I know who you are. Your message has preceded you. My good friend Maggie told me all about how you are bartering to acquire her bicycle. Welcome to my abode, youngsters. By the by, my name is Agnes."

She backed up and waved them into her small home, which was neat as a pin. They entered the living room and saw two antique China cabinets full of nick-knacks and old-fashioned glassware. The carpet was the most beautiful pastel teal color with slightly pink flower patterns here and there.

She waved them over to the color-coordinated couch, saying, "Have a seat. Make yourselves at home, boys. Now, what do you have to swap today?" Hugh liked the way she spoke up and controlled the conversation with such grace.

Hugh carefully unwrapped the paperback book and held it out to her with a hopeful look on his face. She admired the book cover and then flipped slowly through the pages. Agnes said, "Well, well, well! This is right up my alley."

Hugh asked Agnes, "What would you want in exchange? What sort of thing do you have that would be easy for me to trade later on?"

Hugh looked around at all the beautiful things Agnes owned. How was he to know what to pick? He did not have a clue. Hugh said, "Maybe you should tell me what you think I would be happy with. I need a quality item that will be in demand."

So, Agnes walked around the living room and touched a lot of different items. She reached into the first China cabinet and lifted things up, and set them back down. She noticed a cream pitcher with flowers painted on the side. Agnes raised it up high for Hugh to see. She said, "This is a beautiful antique cream pitcher, but a rambunctious great-grandchild broke the matching sugar bowl. Would you be willing to switch your household book for this creamer?"

"Oh, yes, Mam"! Hugh exclaimed. The China creamer was exquisite and looked very expensive. They chatted for quite a while, and Eduardo took their photo. Agnes flashed a provocative smiley look while Hugh presented a silly grin. They held hands while exchanging the Reader's Digest paperback book for the China cream pitcher with flowers painted on the side.

Agnes said, "Now, let me make a phone call to Laurie Ann. Her sister passed away and left boxes of interesting items from her estate. Laurie Ann has plenty of trappings, and she needs to get rid of most of them. I suppose she would welcome the chance to assist you with your trading adventure." So, Agnes did make the phone call, and Laurie Ann did think it was an excellent idea to wheel-and-deal with Hugh and Eduardo. The boys got the directions, memorized them, and headed further North towards Laurie Ann's home.

While they walked a mile and a half towards Laurie Ann's place, Hugh asked Eduardo why he did not present his object to Agnes? He might have missed out on a trade.

Eduardo said, "I might have been a little embarrassed if I showed her this dangerous-looking scorpion embedded in clear acrylic. It would not go well with all the fine antiques she had in her trailer." He stuffed the scorpion into his pocket out of sight.

Hugh said, "You know, I think you were right. That was a good call, my friend."

Chapter 9

Crocheted Granny Throw

It was quite a ways further to Laurie Ann's trailer. The boys were talking about the affairs of the world, so they arrived in no time. They were chuckling about the scorpion as they walked up the driveway. There was Laurie Ann, standing on the landing waving a welcome to them.

"Hello, boys. I'm Laurie Ann. Welcome to my palace. Come on in, and I'll show you what I've got to exchange for that cream pitcher. And what do they call you two?"

"I'm Eduardo, and this is my buddy, Hugh."

She said, "Come on over here. Look at all this stuff my sister left me. You can pick anything you want in these boxes of junk. Look at all my inherited bizarre expendable badunkadunk. Let me see the creamer, please. Oh, boy! This creamer is a beaut. And Eduardo, do you have anything to swap today?"

He answered, "Yes, I want to trade this for something." Eduardo held up the scorpion embedded in a rectangle of clear acrylic.

Laurie Ann scrunched up her face and said, " Why I declare, that is the ugliest thing I have ever seen." Then she stated that it was perfect. "I will give it to give to my little grandson over in Tucson." She snatched the scorpion out of Eduardo's hand, saying, "This is the ideal gift for little Tad." She said he should check out all the useless crud in the boxes.

"Just take whatever appeals to you. My sis left me all this stuff when she departed this world. Since she has deserted us and gone to the great grand beyond, I do need to dispose of these remnants. Go on! Get in there and start digging."

Eduardo joined Hugh, who was already searching through the jumble of junk in the boxes. There were all kinds of things that neither of the boys had ever seen. There was so much stuff. What in the world was the function of all these excess items? Eduardo did not know the purpose of all this stuff. Neither did Hugh. They had no idea who would need these strange things. They picked up unusual things and studied them. They said, "Hummmm, look at this, I wonder what this could be, Huh, Whaaaat, Look at this weird stuff, Stranger than strange, Hmmm, Unusual!"

Finally, in the last cardboard box, Hugh saw something he recognized. It was a crocheted throw with granny squares crocheted into the colorful design. It had a white background with pastel-colored flower patterns in a checkerboard pattern. He considered that it was worth way more than the cream pitcher. But Laurie Ann did not want to keep it, so he decided this was the thing he should choose. Hugh thought that it would be easy to find a new owner for this granny throw. He held it up high and spread it out. How nice it looked! Nothing was wrong with it that Hugh could see.

Meanwhile, Eduardo was still digging through the boxes to see what he could find. He saw metal items. He saw bundles of fabric. He saw wooden carvings. He saw strange crap. He saw unusual junk. He saw plastic stuff. He saw stacks of papers. He saw weird objects. He saw ridiculous things. He saw uncommon rubbish.

Finally, he saw an item that he knew he could trade. He retrieved it from the bottom of the last box. That's right! It was the last thing in the last box at the last minute.

Laurie Ann set her two new treasures on the kitchen table and thanked the boys. "You boys have made my day. I am glad to see you have made great selections, too. My sister had some outlandish stuff, to say the least. Now, it is best if you toddle on home as it will be dark soon. Here, Hugh, let me put that throw in this plastic bag. My sister crocheted it herself and loved covering up with it on cool evenings. You can be sure the new owner will enjoy it for many years. Here is a bag for your selection, too, Eduardo." She stuffed the thing he chose into the large plastic bag.

Laurie Ann said, "I am so delighted to be shed of two more pieces of my sister's property, and I am glad to have the scorpion and the creamer."

"Wait a minute," said Hugh, "Let's take a few snapshots. "They took turns posing for some photographs to remember the occasion. The boys said their goodbyes and walked down the dusty road towards Eduardo's home. The colorful Arizona sunset was magnificent, the wind whistled through the desert landscape, and the pink-tipped black clouds menaced in the southern sky as the two happy boys made tracks down the perfectly straight dirt road.

Chapter 10

Black Cowboy Hat

The Monsoons brought relief to the Sonoran Desert as some of the summer heat abated. Rains came with the Monsoon's rushing winds. In a few short days, things greened up. Flowers popped out here, there, and everywhere. The dead-looking desert came alive from the downpours.

That clear Saturday morning, Hugh went to Arizona City with his dad, who decided to visit a few yard sales. Yard sales are the in thing in Arizona. You can get just about anything you want at yard sales. Hugh had his freshly washed granny throw in a nice-looking bag. His mom had told him when things look respectable and smell fresh, it is easier to find them a new home.

Eduardo could not come with Hugh as he was on his way to visit his grandparents in Tucson. Eduardo planned to continue his swapping business while visiting relatives in Tucson. He had a large extended family who certainly had many extra belongings to exchange.

Meanwhile, Hugh and his dad, Monty, drove up Sunland Gin Road. They passed cotton fields, milo fields, and alfalfa by the mile. An extensive irrigation system allowed these farms to thrive in the middle of the desert. Farmers work long hours to produce money crops. The cotton grown here is made into our clothes and fabrics. The milo goes into chicken and cattle feed. The alfalfa is harvested in bales for animal feed. Even the cotton seeds go into cattle feed.

Sunland Gin Road goes straight north through Arizona City, Arizona, which has a fascinating history. Unusual things happened there during World War Two.

Hugh saw a sign for a yard sale just as they entered the little town from the South. Monty turned the pickup to the right and followed the signs to the yard sale. Yard sale signs are often painted on small cardboard boxes that are placed out by the street. When a large rock or a brick is placed in the brown box, it cannot easily blow away in the wind.

As they drove up and parked by the edge of the paved street, Hugh was scanning the items on display. Out front, he could see a small child's tricycle that had seen better days. It was scratched and faded. Over in the back, he noticed a rack loaded with adult clothing. He quit looking through the open window and prepared to take a closer look.

Hugh jumped out and made a beeline for the yard with all kinds of duds assembled on tables, in boxes, and piled onto tarps. He and his dad had a good time admiring all the used household items. Monty bought himself a blue plaid cowboy shirt that accentuated his blue eyes. It had pearly snaps on the pockets and long tails for tucking in at the waist.

Monty needs long tails because he is a tall guy.

Hugh did not see anything he wanted. They drove a few blocks until they discovered another yard sale along the quiet street. They slowly wandered around, looking at everything piled on tables and tarps. Hugh saw a treasure chest and asked his dad if he would spring for a dollar. Monty said, "Why sure, son. Every boy needs a treasure chest."

With the four borrowed quarters, Hugh paid the teenaged boy who was running that section of the yard sale. Judging by the sorts of belongings for sale there, the young man was getting rid of his childish items to make way for more manly things.

At another yard sale, Monty noticed that practically everything there had been the possessions of an elderly gentleman. There were four expensive suits hanging on a rack. Shiny shoes, super clean white shirts, neckties, polo shirts with color-coordinated shorts, and assorted nice clothing were displayed on tables. Cuff links and tie clips sat in tiny white boxes nearby.

Monty told Hugh, "Look over there. What is that black thing?"

Hugh saw the classy cowboy hat resting on the head of a mannequin. Hugh inspected it with Monty. Father and son went over to talk to the lady who was running the yard sale. They made small talk as is the custom until Hugh asked her about the cowboy hat. While Monty spoke with the lady, Hugh dashed over to the truck to retrieve the granny throw.

Hugh held the granny throw across his forearms and asked the lady if she would be willing to swap the black cowboy hat for this hand-crocheted throw. The lady took one look at the throw and exclaimed, "Oh, my. What a wonderful throw. Let me see that for a second." She gently lifted it up off Hugh's arms and spread it out to get a good look at it.

She said, "It is perfect, but I'm not sure it would be a good exchange."

Then, sharp as a tack, Hugh returned with, "It is probably worth more than the hat. So, you could sell it for more money."

The lady pondered that for a minute and then agreed to the deal. Hugh put on the cowboy hat while the lady admired the throw. Hugh told her that it was hand-crocheted by Laurie Ann's sister.

Monty snapped a picture of Hugh wearing the black cowboy hat standing with the lovely lady holding the hand-crocheted granny throw.

Monty told Hugh, "Come on, lad, we have places to go and people to do."

They thanked the lady again, profusely, and went on their merry way.

Chapter 11

Ten Bolos

On Sunday after lunch, with renewed vigor, Hugh set out to find someone to trade for his classy cowboy hat. As usual, it was hot. This time of day was too hot to wear the cowboy hat. He carried the bagged clean hat in his hand as he trudged down the dusty roads.

The lots are big here in Silverbell, about three acres each, and most of them have nothing on them. The vacant land is still a wild place with rabbits, chipmunks, desert rats, and other natural inhabitants. They are still covered in brush and unused by human beings. So, the few house trailers and doublewides are quite far apart. Often the nearest neighbor is half a mile away. You can see that Hugh put on many miles in his quest for a person willing to trade with him. He walked and talked with every person he could.

Because of the heat, most people were indoors enjoying the cool air conditioning. Hugh knocked on the doors of people he knew, and he knocked on the doors of complete strangers. He told his story over and over many times that afternoon. Hugh did not hear anything he wanted to hear. All he heard was, "No! No, thank you. No, siree. Thank you, but no. Don't bother me, kid. Can't you see I'm busy? Go away. Nope, not interested. No. I don't wear hats."

At a tiny old blue trailer, he did get an encouraging word or two. Sherry, the young lady there, said that her hubby, David has a birthday coming up next week and she would like to give him the hat. The cowboy hat would make a superb gift. She said, "David would look soooooo very outstanding in that hat. I would want him to try it on to make sure it fits right, though. He would want to see that it is the right hat for him."

Hugh knew Sherry and David because he had seen them many times at the fun monthly square dance over at the pavilion. Families, couples on dates, anyone, and everyone frequents the dances. Huge and his buddies often stand around goofing off rather than dancing with the girls. The boys might be wasting time, or they may be learning from each other. If the girls are wallflowers, what are the boys?

Meanwhile, Sherry put on the hat and admired it in the mirror on the trailer wall.

"Oh, yea! I would just love to see David in this hat. You know, David wears his favorite two bolos, but he has ten others that he never wears. Would you take ten bolos for the hat? Here let me show them to you. I'll just set aside the two that he uses."

She came out of the tiny bedroom with a handful of brown and black woven leather strings. Each one had a decorative clasp holding it together. Sherry held them in a wad by their clasps. All the strings were hanging down from her delicate fingers.

Hugh said, "I sure like these shoelace neckties. We sometimes call them string ties. What do you call them, Miss Sherry?"

She said, "We just call them bolos."

Hugh looked through the pile of bolos. He held one up to his throat and admired it in the mirror on the wall. The handmade silver clasp was just right.

The young lady said, "You know, I think it would be apropos for David to pay for his own birthday present. He should be back at any minute. It is so hot; if you want a glass of ice-cold lemonade, we can wait for him over here by the window."

So, they sat in front of the fan at the quaint kitchen table, drinking iced lemonade and chatting. Sherry told Hugh all about how she had to drive so far to take a class in town. She told him it will be worth it because she will make more money with a new skill. She showed him her notebook full of information she is studying for her soon-to-be new, better, higher-paying job.

Sure enough, as promised, they saw David come barreling up in a voluminous cloud of dust. He clomped the dirt off his boots outside the door. He knew Sherry did not care to have dust tracked into their happy little home on wheels.

"What do we have here?" He asked when he saw Hugh sitting at the table.

Sherry said, "This is Hugh. You remember him from the dances at the pavilion. He is the guy who is delivering your birthday present. Lookie here. What do you think? Try it on."

David gingerly lifted the cowboy hat onto his head in one smooth gesture. It was a perfect fit and made David look manly. He already looked manly, but now he looked even more manly.

Sherry admired the black cowboy hat on David's head and said, "Honey, you look too cool!"

Hugh and Sherry both nodded their heads as David stared approvingly at his reflection in the mirror.

David said, "I am surprised as all get out. How did you know that I wanted a bonnet just like this for my birthday? Oh, yea. I do absolutely like it! I wonder where we will get the money to pay for this black beauty?"

Sherry held up the handful of bolos, with their strings swinging down, saying, "These, my dear. We will swap these unused bolos for the bonnet. Don't worry. Your two favorites are still safely in your drawer."

David took the few steps into the tiny bedroom to check on his two prize shoestring neckties. There they were, just like Sherry said they were, two bolos sleeping soundly in his drawer.

Sherry said, "Then it's a deal." She found a plastic bag in the cupboard and stuffed the ten bolos into it. "You are a lifesaver, Hugh. I didn't have a clue what was I going to give David for his birthday? Now the stress is gone. Yippee!"

"Let's take our picture if you don't mind," Hugh said. So, they posed, and Hugh posed for another couple of pictures with each of them. He stuffed the bolos back in the plastic bag again and bid them farewell. From the corner of his alert eye, Hugh noticed David glancing at himself in the mirror on the wall. Hugh chuckled and smiled as he proceeded out the driveway and started up the caliche road.

Hugh saw two beady little eyes at the entrance to an animal hole at the roadside. Probably a packrat or a ground squirrel keeping an eye on his world. Hugh continued walking up the road on his way home. With the sun setting in the majestic trillion-dollar sky, he was rolling over the events of the day in his mind. He heard, No, no, no, no, no, no! His determination paid off. He had listened to a lot of no, no, noes, but in the end, perseverance paid off. He had made a good trade—the cowboy hat for ten bolos. Count them, ten bolos.

Chapter 12

Gorilla Cart

It was still twilight when Hugh returned home. A lone coyote trotted across their yard as he walked up the driveway. Supper was sure a welcome sight that night. Hugh was hungry after a big day walking up and down the spread-out community talking to people.

While the family was eating supper, Hugh showed them the bolos. "Look, folks, at what I traded the cowboy hat for!" Mom and Dad approved of the swap he had made with Sherry. The string neckties were beautiful, and a few were real silver. The majority of the clutches were made of stainless steel.

His parents were proud of him. They heard all about the significant number of people who had said, "No." They listened to all the details about the most important person, Sherry, the young lady who said, "Yes!" She turned the tide of Hugh's fortunes.

When Hugh had finished his account of events, his dad said, "By the way, today, a lady named Lupita called. She heard what you are doing and has a request. She must get rid of her Gorilla Cart and wonders what you have to trade. I suggest you call her up right away. It is a genuine Gorilla Cart!"

Hugh called the phone number immediately after eating. Lupita told him that she has a Gorilla Cart that she must eliminate from her implement collection. She set out the details describing its capabilities. It is tough and strong, and it can haul a heavy load around the yard. It is in excellent condition.

Lupita said they took good care of it and only used it to carry bricks and mortar when they were doing construction on the walls of their house. Now that the work was complete, they had no further use for the Gorilla Cart.

Hugh was excited to get together, and so was Lupita when she heard what Hugh had to swap.

"Oh, Hugh! That is perfect. I can give bolos to all my male relatives for Christmas presents. There won't be any left over to give to my friends. You know what a large family we have. Of course, I will want to check them out before we make a final decision," She remarked.

Hugh asked her if she would be home tomorrow. When she answered in the affirmative, they made an appointment to meet up.

Hugh got on the phone shortly with his pal Eduardo. They were talking over each other, swapping exciting stories about their swapping up weekend. Eduardo came home with a strange item. Over the weekend, he had been able to coerce some of his distant relatives into making trades. Even though they had no interest in swapping, Eduardo made them see the light. Since he was a kid on a mission and since he was their "favorite," didn't they have a responsibility to help him out? Ha, ha, finally, they came around to his way of thinking. Eduardo had to wheel and deal with his savvy relatives until he made some excellent bargains.

On Monday morning Hugh and Eduardo walked the three miles over to Lupita's doublewide with the brand-new real brick siding. The new walls were freshly laid dusty pink bricks and looked fabulous.

When Lupita saw the ten bolos, she was pleased, as were the boys when they inspected the Gorilla Cart. Eduardo took four photos of the swap. Of course, Hugh had to sit in the cart and act goofy while Lupita gladly held the bolos up for everyone to see. They both had big toothy smiles on their faces. You could see that it was a primo trade for each of them.

Lupita reaffirmed that her male relatives would be happy at Christmas when they open their presents and see elegant western string neckties. Out West, men often wear bolos when they get dressed up. The boys drank water from the garden hose before setting out for home. Taking turns pulling the Gorilla Cart and riding, they talked rambunctiously. They passed the time as they proceeded down the perfectly straight road, exchanging stories of conquest and swiping the sweat from their brows as the sun lowered in the western sky.

They were happy-go-lucky guys. They knew they were in control of their destinies.

Chapter 13

Hand-made Kachina Doll

Both boys were working at overcoming their reticence when speaking with others. Neither of them was shy, but each was a little reluctant to walk right up and talk to people. So, they practiced on each other. Two guinea pigs, they were making good manners a habit and becoming unguarded in their conversations with others. They practiced and, over time, perfected their short speeches.

Hugh let Eduardo know what a respectable job he was doing, making so many swaps over the weekend, and Eduardo told Hugh the same thing. They were two consciously determined boys. Hugh sure wanted that bicycle, while Eduardo had nothing in particular that he desired to acquire. He just wanted to make trades for things that were superior and grander. At this moment, he was just interested in swapping up, and they both were getting bigger and better things.

Eduardo came home with Hugh, and they had a good time playing with the Gorilla Cart and messing around. Hugh wondered out loud where he could find a person who wanted a Gorilla Cart. It could be a problem. Who would want a Gorilla Cart?

Days passed with no results. Hugh and Eduardo pulled the Gorilla Cart up and down the roads asking everyone what they had to trade. Nothing was acceptable. They asked at a house building site, but the construction workers said they used a Skid-steer to move materials.

Hugh and Eduardo were a little gloomy when they returned with the Gorilla Cart in tow, as they had done on too many previous days.

Meanwhile, Hugh's Mom, Melanie, told the boys that she had just had a great idea.

"Tell us! Tell us!" That was all that they could say.

She laid it out, "You remember our old friends who are building their house from dirt? They carry dirt to fill bags, Earth Bag Construction, they call it. Big bags of soil are stacked up one upon another to form walls. I bet you fifty cents that they would be dying to have your Gorilla Cart. I'm going to call up Wendy right now and see what she has to say!"

And so, she did. Melanie found Wendy taking a break, and they had a quick talk on the phone. Wendy and Wyatt, her ever-loving husband, had to get back to work filling feed bags full of dirt as soon as possible.

Not far from Kitts Peak, Wendy and Wyatt were at a higher elevation. It was not so extremely hot over there in Pima County. However, it was hot enough to be troublesome when laboring energetically outdoors. Melanie made arrangements to come to visit and possibly make a trade. Wendy and Wyatt were all excited about the possibility of another Gorilla Cart and a visit from dear friends, of course.

Hugh and Eduardo wanted to know what Wendy and Wyatt had to swap. They were surprised when Melanie told them they had choices to make when they arrived at the construction site. Decisions, Decisions.

Monty wanted to go too so he could visit his long-time friends. The trip would have to wait until the weekend when Monty will be off work. They all waited patiently. Well, not patiently. But they waited! And they had to find other occupations for the time being. Hugh and Eduardo studied the Spanish language book. The boys practiced Spanish with each other. Taking turns, they also read *One Red Paperclip* from end to end. They even read out loud to each other.

Pima County is a rugged place in Arizona where this couple is building with the Earth Bag Construction method. They fill feed sacks full of dirt from their own property and stack them up to construct a dome-shaped house. They previously created an underground, cool root cellar to store their supplies. They even built an underground water storage tank to catch the occasional rainwater. They were not on a water system, and they did not have a water well either.

At the time of this writing, Wendy and Wyatt are constructing a dome with a living room and a workspace. Wyatt uses his Gorilla Cart to haul dirt. Do you think they could use another Gorilla Cart? Hugh thinks they need one more Gorilla Cart, and he will be the one to bring it to them.

Melanie looked it up and found it was a two-hour drive from Silverbell to their friend's property. The little family was looking forward to going.

"Don't forget to take the Gorilla Cart," Hugh was reminding himself. He made sure that Eduardo would tag along with them, too.

Finally, on Saturday before sunrise Melanie, Monty, and the two boys were on their way. They arrived around 8 am and got the Gorilla Cart out of the pickup bed. There were hugs all around.

Wyatt and Wendy looked the Gorilla Cart over really well. They even loaded it up with dirt and evaluated its capabilities. It was strong and worked reliably.

The guests admired the walls that were under construction. Amazing! Simple elegance. Hugh and Eduardo served up frosty canned drinks that were on ice in the cooler. Wyatt and Wendy allowed their friends to help with the work for only the next four hours.

Today Wyatt was mixing adobe for them to slap onto the wall formed of earthbags stacked up high. If the bright sun shines on the bags too long, they begin to degrade, causing the wall to come apart.

From a large pile, Monty dug dirt with a shovel. Earth had to be put through a screen to separate rocks and dirt clods that were too large. The smooth soil fell into the cart while the stones and clods landed in a particular separate spot.

Monty tugged the half-full Gorilla Cart over to the tarp lying on the ground, where he made a pile of dirt. He used the dump function to let the dirt fall out. The Gorilla Cart's dumping function makes it easy to unload.

Using a shovel, Wyatt placed some dirt and straw into his cement mixer with the perfect amount of water to make a mix that was not too thin and not too thick. He dumped the globby mixture out into a wheelbarrow for Wendy to use as adobe plaster. She gathered a couple of pounds at a time and plopped it onto the outside of the earthbags. She mashed and patted and pushed the mud into place on the exterior of the building. This is her method of plastering the stucco walls of the new house to keep the sun rays off the feed bags.

It is imperative that they completely cover the feed sacks with this mud-straw stucco mixture. When the sun bears down on bags for too long, the UV Rays will begin to disintegrate them, which will eventually lead to the destruction of the entire building. Now that would be heart-breaking, not to mention a complete waste of time, energy, and money.

Melanie and the boys helped Wendy for a considerable time. After a while, they were getting low on dirt, so the boys grabbed shovels, switched jobs, and began to help Monty gather more dirt. Using both Gorilla Carts, they were able to double the amount of dirt transferred. Meanwhile, Wyatt continued doing his master mud-material-making mission. Now they had a system that was working like clockwork. All of them kept occupied as dirt diggers, adobe-maker, and the ladies packing the sloppy, messy stucco onto the outside of the wall.

The stacked-up earthbags began to disappear under the muddy plaster. The friends worked and worked and talked and talked. Before they knew it, time was up. That was a quick four hours.

In the allotted time, they had accomplished something significant. They had a good time working together with their friends, but they had to stop before getting too sore. They didn't want to have painful blisters on their hands.

Wendy suggested that they find something to trade for the Gorilla Cart. Wyatt said he and Monty would take care of lunch. Everyone was hungry. Hongray!

Wendy started showing them a few items they had on hand. Out under the carport, they had an extra couch. Hugh and Eduardo looked at each other and said together, "No, that is nice, but it would be too big to haul around to show to people."

They went into the small camping trailer to find something better.

"Let me show you this quilt that my grandma made. The assorted colors are exceptionally bright." Melanie loved the quilt, but the boys said, "Thanks, it is so pretty but not this time."

Wendy showed them the Jackalope that always sat behind them when they were recording their podcast. "No, we wouldn't think of depriving you of your infamous Jackalope," Hugh said.

Then Wendy set a two-foot-long box on the kitchen table in front of Hugh.

"Hugh asked Wendy, "What's in there?"

"Take a look," Wendy told him.

That is just what he did. Hugh peeked inside the prone flat box and was amazed to see a Kachina Doll looking back at him.

Wendy told them the story of how her great aunt had made stunning Kachina Dolls all by hand. Now her diligence and skill could pay off. A swap for the Gorilla Cart is needed to make the work easier here at the homestead.

A rare Kachina Doll in a box is valuable but cannot help them build a house.

Hugh decides, "Okay, it is final," he says. "If you want to trade, I want to trade."

Wendy handled and looked at each and every part of the Kachina. She admired the art and beauty of each section of the doll. She stroked the feathers and petted the face. Wendy kissed the doll goodbye. Melanie grabbed her camera and asked Wendy and Hugh to pose with the Gorilla Cart and the extraordinary, handmade Kachina Doll. Everyone went outdoors and gathered around as they wanted to be in the picture, too.

Hugh put the Kachina Doll back in the box and carried it out to the extended cab pickup truck.

He put it in the truck's back seat, where the boys sit while traveling. He made sure to shut the windows to keep the dust off his Kachina Doll.

Everyone was saying how marvelous the doll was. Wyatt admired the Gorilla Cart and appreciated all the work it could do. He proclaimed that they were all winners.

All of them were hungry, so they set up a card table and some folding chairs inside the unfinished dome, where the adults sat down to lunch provided by Wyatt and Monty. Eduardo and Hugh sat on overturned buckets nearby with food in their laps. They ate and lounged around in the shade for a few hours, remembering old times, telling jokes, and cutting up. Hugh and Eduardo kept all the glasses full of ice and soft drinks. The boys heard things they had never heard before. They heard passages that they did not think were possible from the adults. Sometimes it helps to have listening ears.

Chapter 14

Jewelry

After the outing to see their friends, things have returned to normal, hot and windy, dusty and gritty. Back in Silverbell, Hugh keeps thinking about the Kachina Doll and trying to find someone who wants to swap. He and Eduardo put on many miles in the village.

The two boys walked up and down the checkerboard pattern of roads. They asked everyone in the area if they would like to trade, but there were no takers. They returned to all the homes where they had been before. They might have been discouraged. Did they find a swapper? Did they give up?

No, no such thing!

However, things turned around when Melanie answered the phone one fine day. The nosey boys listened intently.

Excitement filled the air! Hugh shouted, "Whoooo, hoooo! Whoooo, hoooo!"

Eduardo said, "Way to go! That's so cool."

Who was on the phone, and what did she want?

It turned out that a nice lady had heard through the grapevine that Hugh had an extraordinary, handmade Kachina Doll to sell. Being a big-time doll collector, she was interested in buying it for cash money. She said that, unfortunately, she did not have anything to trade at this time.

Hugh's face fell. Eduardo's face looked shocked. By her expression, Melanie was obviously disappointed, but she did have the presence of mind to write down the lady's phone number and her name.

Hugh asked, "What are we going to do, Mom?"

She said, "You can try to work something out with her or keep looking for someone who will trade something other than money."

Hugh asked, "What to do? What to do?"

Eduardo said, "Just sleep on it."

Without a definitive answer, they let it go for now, and Eduardo left for home.

Suddenly, in the middle of that night, the drought was broken. The noisy Monsoon rains inundated the dried-up landscape. Water gathered in low spots and ran down the washes.

The desert was glorious, with scattered showers, huge strange colored clouds, and rainbows for the next few days. The cacti and brush soaked up every drop of water. The rain rinsed all the dust off the plants making everything look fresh and new. Caterpillars were crawling here and there. The lizards' bellies were extremely fat. There goes one running for cover with a giant yellow caterpillar hanging from his mouth.

The Saguaros soaked up the moisture to become swollen while the Creosote sprang into life with greenery. Frogs left their holes looking for ponds and swales that filled with water. There they laid eggs which quickly hatched. The tadpoles grew fast and lost their tails, turning into little frogs before the ponds became hard and dry again.

Meanwhile, Hugh thought about the offer. Perhaps he

should accept the cash and then pay money for the bicycle. Maybe he should ask the lady to find a necklace to trade for the Kachina Doll. Hugh kept mulling it over in his mind. There were so many possibilities. He could always take the money and go shopping for a necklace to trade for the bike. Hugh had promised Maggie that he would bring jewelry, and that is what he plans to do.

It was a few days later that the lady called again. She said that her grown son had acquired the most beautiful set of emerald jewelry. It included a gorgeous stone set in a necklace, a matching emerald bracelet, and a pair of classy green earrings.

She asked, "How can we get together to check things out?"

Hugh's Mom got on the phone to make arrangements to meet.

So, the following Saturday, on their usual day to go to town, Melanie, Hugh, and Eduardo went to the lady's home near Casa Grande. It was lovely, neat, clean, and spiffy. Nevertheless, the lady apologized, saying, "Please excuse the mess. I have been working overtime all this past month."

Hugh and Eduardo chuckled under their breath. They had never been in such a magnificent house before in their lives. It was a big and beautiful Spanish Style home. The ceilings were vaulted, and the rooms were huge. Someone decorated it all in Western Style. There were genuine ancient artifacts on display everywhere you looked.

The lady invited them to sit at the kitchen table, where she laid out the emerald jewelry on a plain bath towel for Hugh to see.

The group was all enthralled with the jewelry set. They oohed and awed. "Would you look at that! How precious!"

Then Hugh opened the two-foot-tall box to expose the hand-made Kachina Doll lying inside. The lady quickly grabbed a clean bath towel to lay it on. They all admired it, and the lady said, "Ooh! Awe! Oooooooh! It is especially fanciful! I just adore it. How precious it is."

Both parties wanted to trade right then and there, but they decided the smart thing to do would be to get them appraised. In Casa Grande, the best place for honest, accurate appraisals is the pawnshop.

The lady said, "We can go in my car." So, with the valuables in the trunk, they all piled into the luxury sedan. Off they drove to the local pawn shop where the most knowledgeable man in town spent most of his time.

After the sole lingering customer left the shop, our party eagerly set their items on the counter. They laid out the clean towels first, of course.

Roy, the pawnshop owner, looked at the Kachina Doll first. He admired all the fine qualities and liked the fact that it had a little engraved plaque on it naming the person who made it and the date, too.

Roy said, "I would value this Kachina at $240.

Next, he looked at the vintage emerald jewelry set. He

used his eye magnifier to scrutinize the pieces. He thought the set looked familiar.

"Wait just a minute," Roy declared. "This is the set of emerald jewelry we had that went missing the other day!"

Everyone was surprised as they looked at each other in disbelief.

The stunned nice lady said, "That does not sound right. My son, Cecil, brought them home to me this past week. He is an honest young man. I could call him and see if he will zip over here. Cecil works just up the street."

She called and asked her son if he had the receipt for the emerald jewelry.

Cecil said, "I think it is still in my wallet. Let me check. Yes, yes, it is right here. Give me two shakes of a lamb's tail, and I'll be right there to the pawnshop."

The nice lady wondered what was going on.

Melanie figured something strange was transpiring.

Hugh thought, "Why is this happening to me?"

Eduardo reckoned that you don't always get what you want.

The stunned group anxiously waited, but her son arrived shortly.

Cecil handed the receipt to Roy, who studied it carefully.

Directly, Roy said, "Well, I'll be hornswoggled! It says right here that Cecil bought it last week and paid by credit card. Right here in my pawnshop."

Roy searched busily through his records and found what he needed.

"Cecil did buy the jewelry here, but my inept clerk did not properly record the substantial price he paid," explained Roy to the flabbergasted group. They all became relieved to know they did not need to be worried about any shenanigans going on.

Roy gave the receipt back to Cecil. It showed that it would be a fair trade to both parties if they swapped items.

Each one shook hands with Roy and thanked him enthusiastically. Cecil said he would bring a copy of the receipt to Roy just to be on the safe side.

They made the trade, and everyone posed for pictures at the pawnshop before returning to the Spanish Style House. Hugh thanked the nice lady exuberantly for keeping in touch and providing the jewelry he needed to retrieve the bicycle.

The nice lady thanked them profusely again and posed for more pictures. She was thrilled with the trade they had made. She held her prized Kachina Doll safely under her arm and waved as she went in her front door.

The old pickup truck carried the happy threesome to town quickly. Melanie had her shopping list, Hugh had his emerald jewelry set neatly packed in its luxurious box, and Eduardo had an enormous appetite for ice cream. So, just to be affable, each one enjoyed a vanilla cone along with him.

Chapter 15

Bicycle

On the way home from shopping, they could not stop at Maggie's trailer. The cold and frozen food had to be put in the refrigerator and freezer right away. It was a long hot trip from the grocery store to home. Because of the blazing hot weather, Melanie kept her cold food in ice chests in the back of the truck. She did not want her food to melt, defrost, and spoil on the 35-mile drive to Silverbell.

The boys helped put away the groceries. Into the freezer went the frozen food first. Then the cold food went into the refer. The foodstuffs they put away last were the dry goods and canned products, which they placed in the pantry and cupboards.

"Mom, would you drive us over to Maggie's place? I'm itching to see how she likes this necklace set."

She said, "Come on, boys, jump in the truck."

Hugh clung to the boxed jewelry as they bumped down the dirt road. The thick dust whirled as they entered Maggie and Ellie's driveway and stepped out of the truck. Hugh was not the only one spitting out sand. All three of them had grit in their teeth.

"Maggie, Maggie!" shouted Hugh as the boys ran up to the door of the house trailer. Ellie came quickly to the door, but Maggie came rumbling slowly after her.

"Do come in. Come on in," the ladies said. "Pull up a chair by the fire!"

They all laughed because they wanted to be right in front of the air conditioner on a blistering hot day like today.

Hugh said, "Wait until you see what I brought for you, Miss Maggie."

He set the expensive-looking box on the little old pink linoleum-topped kitchen table. The rectangle table was definitely from a different era of time. Hugh gently and deliberately laid the vintage genuine emerald jewelry set out precisely for all to see. It was quite a sight to behold! The pieces were stunning. Maggie would have to be crazy not to love them.

Maggie had tears in her green eyes as she reached over to touch the necklace. She held up each piece separately and admired the designs.

The green gemstones were bright and sparkled in the sun streaming through the windows near the table.

"Oh my," she said. "This is unparalleled richness!"

She held the earrings next to the sides of her head. Then she put the bracelet on her thin, freckled wrist. She said, "Oh my, I am at a loss for words."

"Oh my! I am speechless," she emphasized her statement.

At that moment, with a glint in his eye, Hugh said, "Then I guess you don't care for this set."

Ellie smacked him on the hand that was reaching for the necklace.

"Get your grimy paws off that. Of course, she loves it and wants to swap with you." Everyone in the room laughed out loud. Even the old grey mare out in the nearby corral joined in the laughter.

They took plenty of pictures that evening as they completed the swap. Maggie still had tears in her eyes when she put on the necklace and earrings. She admired herself in the floor-to-ceiling mirror. She rolled around in her wheelchair to let everyone see how lovely the gems looked. She proudly exhibited her treasures. They all took a good look and approved of what they saw.

All of them gave Maggie the profuse compliments that she deserved.

Meanwhile, Hugh rode his bicycle around the driveway with a silly grin on his face.

As time went by, Hugh enjoyed riding his bike at breakneck speeds all over the rural village of Silverbell. Now he possessed his very own bicycle, and he was one happy-go-lucky boy.

Hugh started with a tiny bottle and swapped up to bigger and better things. Even though he sometimes felt bashful, he stubbornly searched and scouted around until he found a trader. The determined boy swapped up until he eventually landed a trade for the bike of his dreams.

Hugh put himself forward just like you can do. A person can't just sit at home and expect prodigious things to happen. To be productive, you must be a mover and a shaker!

Hugh put himself out there where he received no after no answers when he offered items to exchange.

After receiving noes repeatedly, his secret to success was perseverance. Hugh achieved success, and so can you by becoming a swapper extraordinaire. Fortune belongs to the bold.

The prizes belong to those who begin and continue to the end. The starting point is directly in front of your feet. Grab an item, cross over the line, and get out there. Rush across the starting line. Discover how to accumulate your treasures by trading up. Bigger truly is better. Swap up, my friends! Indeed, the delight of swapping up is within your reach.

Shortly, buddy Eduardo also acquired a bicycle, so the two boys teamed up for riding pleasure.

There they go again!
And

There they go again!

You acquired information by osmosis. As you read, you picked up the details of trading from Hugh, who demonstrated how he swapped up from a tiny old bottle to a splendid bicycle.

Hugh accumulated many miles walking everywhere he went. Walking took extra time, but now he can quickly get from place to place riding his magnificent bike.

Swapping up can be adopted by youngsters or oldsters. There is no definitive age limit. If swapping up appeals to you, then go for it!

Just like you, Hugh wanted something unique. He desired to be zooming up and down the roads in his little village on his very own bike.

What is your personal desire? What is your top-secret method for success?

It could be the beneficial use of Swapping Up!

:

Resources:

The photo on the cover of a boy riding a bicycle was purchased from Canva.

Invitation:

You are invited to leave stars and written reviews 24 hours a day in the books section found on Amazon.com. Every review and star helps me to sell more books. Your promoting activity is greatly appreciated.

If you enjoyed this book, tell your friends. If you found it lacking, tell the author.

Notes

Notes

Notes

Notes

Notes

Notes

Notes

Notes